FURRY BIG SISTER

Written by Brittany Oliver
Illustrated by Timna Green

This book is for my parents who made sure I always had two things growing up: unwavering support and pets.

It is for my husband who makes it easy to keep falling in love with him.

It is for my daughter who is bold, cheeky and magnificent.

But mostly this is for you, Bella, my sweet girl.
Thank you for making our house feel like a home… a warm, loving, sometimes stinky, fur-covered one.

For all of my life, it has been just us three:

Alpha Mum, Alpha Dad, little old me.

My life was a wonder, each day a delight,

I had treats in my bowl and was snuggled so tight.

I'd hear "good girl" and "sweet girl" with pats on my head.

I would curl up with the Alphas asleep in my bed.

Early at dawn I'd wake up in the middle,

they'd give me a squeeze, take me out for a piddle.

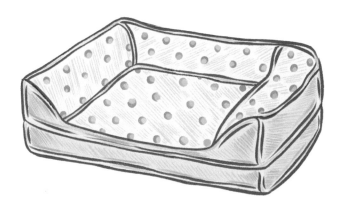

Then off they would go to perform Alpha duties.

And I'd rest, one ear cocked for the sound of their booties.

Protecting the door – oh so patiently waiting,

my water bowl dry and my squeeze toy deflating.

I'd go find a shoe that was left on the floor,
a suitable gift when they opened the door.
My Alphas would pet me with laughter and smiles,
"Hi there, my baby. It's been a long while."

But today something's different, a curious smell.

My Alpha Dad grins and says, "Mum did so well."

Nose up in the blankets, I give them a nudge,

attempting to get the small bundle to budge.

Slowly, but surely, Dad starts to expose,

a wee little face and ten fingers, ten toes.

He says "Just be gentle. Your new sibling is here."

My Alphas smell different. More love, but some fear.

I'm not sure if I want this new bundle to stay.

I give it a lick, but Dad pulls it away.

He looks at my tail to make sure that it wags,

then ushers me out to make room for more bags.

All evening they cuddle it, swinging and swaying.

I bring it a toy but sulk off without playing.

A small pat from Mum as I quietly wait.

My tummy is growling, my dinner is late.

My Alphas look tired as they sing and they rock.

I stare at my leash as it's time for our walk.

To bed we all go, but I'm not allowed up.

I flop on the floor like a good little pup.

Late in the evening, it's time for my treat,

but Alpha Mum asks you, "Oh, why won't you eat?"

Teary and tired, she needs a good nap.

I sit by her side, put my head on her lap.

I am here for you Alpha, for all that you've done.

You've made my life special. You've made the days fun.

Then she lowers the bundle. I take a step back.

I want to inspect this new friend of the pack.

Gently and softly she motions to come,

and what do you know – you look just like Mum!

More days and nights pass, and the trust grows and grows.

Baby Alpha Mum even reaches for my nose.

The cuddles are plenty, relationship built,

and Dad gives me many more treats out of guilt.

You cry and you laugh, and you toot and you coo.

I am rapidly making a friend out of you.

The Alphas seem pleased, as they smile and stare;

tenderly watching the moments we share.

I can't wait to teach you to roll on the floor,

and loudly announce every knock at the door!

I will show you the bowl that we'll both use for eating,

and I'll teach you the most considerate greeting.

As the light of the moon glimmers bright overhead,

I won't let you be lonely – I'll sleep by your bed.

And I promise to guard you when out for our walk,

marching proud by your stroller, around every block.

We pose for Mum's pictures, but it's just a tease.

Not once do I get the agreed upon cheese.

She shows us the photos, and I hear her say,

"It's so you remember your first dog one day."

Still the days come with no time for a pet,

and I hope I'm not something my Alphas regret.

They tell me they love me – it's just you're brand-new.

They say in a way I prepared them for you.

And now when I hear you come in through the door,

my heart and my paws leap right up off the floor!

My bum in a wiggle, my tail like a twister,

happy to be your furry big sister.

The dog years go by, and my coat gets more grey,

there's a little more sleeping, a little less play.

But no need to be sad for your friend on all fours,

you came home to my love, and I'll leave here with yours.

THE END

About the Author

Brittany Oliver lives, writes, and catches babies in Fonthill, Ontario. As a midwife, she gets a privileged glimpse into the magical but grueling early days with a newborn. She has always been moved by budding friendships between family dogs and their human siblings. In fact, this book was inspired by a poem she wrote in 2020, after bringing her own baby home to meet Bella, her fiercely loyal, eleven-year-old Australian shepherd mix.

She hopes that her words can reach as many families as possible. Your honest reviews and comments are incredibly appreciated. Brittany invites you to follow her on social media (Instagram @wit.by.brit) or check out her website witbybrit.com where you can find poems and stories about midwifery and motherhood.

Lightning Source UK Ltd.
Milton Keynes UK
UKHW052056250123
415980UK00001B/1